Jaylynn
The
Creative

Julia A. Royston

BK
ROYSTON
Publishing

BK Royston Publishing
P. O. Box 4321
Jeffersonville, IN 47131
502-802-5385
http://www.bkroystonpublishing.com
bkroystonpublishing@gmail.com

Cover Design: Gad of Elite Book Covers
Image of Jaylynn Designed by: Sanghamitra Dasputa

ISBN-13: 978-1-959543-11-4

Printed in the United States of America

Dedication

I dedicate this book to every creative
person on the planet. You're special.
You're unique. You're a creative.

Remember that Creatives CREATE!

Acknowledgements

First, I acknowledge my Creator for giving me all of my gifts and especially my gift to write.

My husband who is always supportive, loving and encouraging me to utilize all of my gifts and talents. Thank you honey.

To my mother, Dr. Daisy Foree, who is my number one cheerleader and always tells me, "hang in there, you can do it." To my father, Dr. Jack Foree, who is never far away from me in spirit or my heart. I only have to look in the mirror each day to see him.

To Rev. Claude and Mrs. Lillie Royston who support me in everything I do.

To the rest of my family, I love you and thank you for your prayers, support and love.

To the team of BK Royston Publishing and Royal Media and Publishing that make it easier for me to write and publish the books I love, thank you!

Table of Contents

Introduction

My purpose for writing this book is to shine a light and encourage the creatives of this world to keep going and create what's in your head and what only heart can see and feel.

I have been a creative all of my life. From music to writing books, it's down inside of me. I see it, I hear it and I feel it and hopefully the things that I see and feel come through my music and my writings. I guess I'm a little selfish and understand how it feels to be a creative and see other people can the BIG spotlight and only a dim shadow falls on the real creatives behind the scenes. Not anymore!

I see the great potential, intelligence and natural ability that lies in the next generation and I want to make sure that they have the encouragement and continue to have the courage to keep going and growing.

I always want to write, share and publish books that help bring the greatness out of each of you and for the world to see.

Come on creatives, create! Come out of the shadows and into the light! Let the creative light that is within shine bright!

Takes one to know one.

Blessings.

Julia A. Royston

Meet Jaylynn

Hi my name is Jaylynn Harris. I am an only child, which means that all of the attention is on me and has been since I was a child. I am not spoiled in a bad way but pretty spoiled in a very good way. My parents, Garvin and Montana Harris, make sure that I get to do the things that interest me and that I love. There are other things that are required for school that I don't really care for, like sports, running or other physical sports but in my element, I love it. If you were in my room right now, you could easily tell that I love art. I can't really remember when I picked up the first crayon, pencil or paint brush, but each and every day, I can't imagine myself without it. I simply love art. I love to use crayons, pencils, markers, paint brushes and anything else I can get my hands on to make a design, paint a picture or create a story through what I draw or see.

On the other hand, I love to sing and music is also my thing. My mother said that she played soft music while I was still in her stomach and there was always instrumental or soft music playing in my room when I was still in my crib. Music puts me to sleep at night, especially the soft and soothing sounds of a flute, harp or smooth jazz music. I even love calm sounds, like the ocean or soft rain or birds chirping or other smooth sounds. Just sounds that soothe and comfort are definitely for me. I play soft music when I study, paint, draw or create. I learn music but when I am creating music, I need quiet. I can't create music while listening to music. It throws me off and I realize that I am trying to recreate what I hear instead of creating my own sounds that come from my head. When it comes to music, I've got to sit still, wait for the creative juices to flow and then listen.

Since I am an only child, I spend a lot of time alone, but I am not lonely. With my parents in the house, being connected to my friends online as well as at school, I have a wonderful life. We live in the city, with high rise buildings and culture everywhere. My parents have taken me since I was a child to every art museum and gallery in the city. I am interested in all of the painters, sculptors and artists, but my favorite period in art is the Impressionist Period. The art created during that time is wonderful to me. So full of every color in the rainbow. All of the tiny brush strokes that make up each image. All of the images created in so many different ways that it is incredible to see. I hope to be an artist with those same abilities one day. I realize with so many influences and things that I like to do creatively, I am officially a creative. That's what I'll call myself, Jaylynn Harris, the Creative.

Draw a Picture of Your Choice.

Creativity is connected to your head and your heart. Why did you draw it?

_____

_____

_____

_____

_____

_____

_____

_____

_____

_____

_____

_____

_____

_____

_____

_____

_____

Creativity is All in the Family

This creative and art thing is a family affair. Not only do I love art, but my dad loves art too. He creates art in several different ways. Sometimes, he uses just his computer, laptop or other mobile device. Other times, he has to draw it out by pencil or coloring pencils to get his idea down in rough draft format. He is the real technology guru of the family. His work room is down the hall from my bedroom and I love to see him use computers, iPad, phone, drawing pad or anything else he can get his hands on to create, as well as other software. Watching him create inspires me to do my work. There are framed art work of his work hanging on the walls around his office from when he was younger growing up, until he married my mom. He used to paint and draw by hand, but now, it is just primarily his desktop, laptop, iPad, mouse and very vivid imagination.

He creates and designs animation too. He sits at his desk with a mug of coffee on the desk and a half eaten sandwich too. The desk is large enough for two monitors and a small lamp opposite the monitors for better light. There is a small window in his office and only room for a couple of chairs because it is small. I love watching Dad work. I especially love the way he makes everything move by a click of his mouse or an electronic pen that he uses with his iPad. One day, he'll teach me to animate as well. My dream is to one day be in business for myself like my parents. If my dad and I could be in business together, that would be great too. Each day that I wake up and see my dad, I say, "Good morning, Dad."

"Good morning, beautiful," Dad replies. "What are you going to do to create something wonderful today?"

"I don't know yet, but I'm open," I reply.

"That's my girl. Stay open, be inspired and remember that you are a creative."

"Thanks, Dad." I slightly blush, as I know that I am a creative. Who told me first? My dad.

I look over my dad's shoulder for a while as he is already at work on a project for kids. I'm proud of my dad and know that he is proud of me too.

"Well, I've got to go see Mom and then breakfast," I tell him.

"Have a great day."

"I will."

What's something that your entire family loves? For example, sports, music, games, movies or food? Think about it. Draw it below.

What's so great about it? The taste, the action, the sounds or the beat or just being with family??

_____

_____

_____

_____

_____

_____

_____

_____

_____

_____

_____

_____

_____

_____

_____

Home

Our apartment has three bedrooms and three bathrooms. It is very large for an apartment in the city. Normally, people would say that it should probably be a one story house or condo, but it's a very large apartment in my opinion. I don't worry about what others think because it is where I live and I love it. Down the hall is the main living room which is huge and the preferred space and hangout of my mother. My mom rounds out our creative family as a musician and sculptor too.

When we moved into this building, I was just two years old. I remember that the living room was so huge, but Mom said that it would be divided into two and her space. It is large enough for her baby grand piano and the sculpting wheel too. Yes, my mother is a musician and sculptor. What a combination. The sculpting wheel requires water for the clay, so she covers the grand piano so it doesn't get splattered or stained. My mom loves music and sculpting equally. Both of these skills require her hands and she told me that she always loved working with and creating things with her hands as a child. As an adult, it hasn't changed. She taught me to play some songs on the piano. I love music and still play sometimes too, but my first love is art. My mom says that's okay, I can just appreciate both but specialize in the drawing art like my dad. When my mom puts the clay on the wheel, dips her hand in the water and the spinning starts, I stand amazed at what her hands will form with the clay in her hands.

"Hey, Mom," I say as I enter the room.

"Good morning, love, how are you today?"

"Good, I guess?"

"Good, I guess? What's going on?"

"Nothing, just getting my mind ready to head into the school building. See my friends and some not-so-friendly people as well," I say.

"I understand, but education is important to me and your dad. It should also be important to you no matter the other people. Concentrate on you, not the other people, do your best and have some fun too. Make and create something wonderful, okay?"

"Okay."

"Get some breakfast and let me know before you head out so that you are not late for school."

"I will. Love you."

"Love you too. Get going."

I head down the hallway to the kitchen. For breakfast, I grab a Pop Tart, a bottled water, an apple and then yell at mom before I head out the front door to the elevator, "I'm gone, Mom and Dad. Love you both."

They both reply, "I love you too." I'm good for the day just knowing my parents love me. I know it's corny or old-fashioned, but I love my parents. Out of their sight, I now have a smile on my face. I'll get lunch at school later, but right now, I must walk fast as most people do in the city so that I will make it to school on time.

Walking down the street, there are so many different people, smells, noises and sights for a person to behold. Inspiration can come from anywhere. All different kinds of languages are heard in the street, from Spanish to English to Italian back to English to French and back to English again and again. The United States is a melting pot of people, cultures, food and traditions. This is what my parents say are important so that I am a well-rounded individual and able to communicate through what I feel and create to any group of people.

What's your favorite drink for breakfast? Juice, coffee, tea or milk. If you had your own brand for this drink, what would you name it. Draw a picture of it.

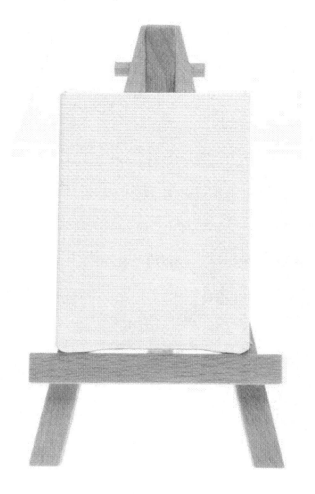

Sip on your favorite drink and journal your thoughts about your day or your life. Let's go!

_____
_____
_____
_____
_____
_____
_____
_____
_____
_____
_____
_____
_____
_____
_____
_____
_____
_____

_____

_____

_____

_____

_____

_____

_____

_____

_____

_____

_____

_____

_____

_____

_____

_____

_____

_____

_____

_____

_____

_____

_____

Hybrid School

Since the COVID pandemic, our school has decided to have hybrid schedule for school. There are some weeks that school is solely online and other times it is held in-person. Just in case something else happens in the world, learning will always be able to continue. I don't mind which way school happens, in-person or online, I love it. In addition to where we live, my parents want me to have a diverse learning environment with ideas and points of view from all different types of people, cultures and backgrounds. Public school is the choice for us as a family. My mother says, "The world is diverse and we will be too."

There are more than fifty languages and dialects spoken in my city as well as ten different languages in my school.

On the virtual or online days, we attend all of the classes by logging into one assigned location. Our schedules are in groups, Group 1, Group 2, Group 3 for each grade. The teachers are assigned to us by grade level, group and class subject. They rotate in and out of the log ins and groups all day long. The students, on the other hand, only have one log in per day. We receive new log ins each and every week on Sunday night prior to school on Monday morning.

This is in-person week and Monday, so I'm hurrying to the school building as fast as my feet will go.

I have two wonderful friends, London and Jackie, whom I hang out with in-person and we are in the same grade and group online. When I walk to my locker, there they both are, my best friends in the world.

"Hey, Jaylynn," London says in greeting.

"Hey, London," I say back to her.

"What's up, Jaylynn? Great to see you in person."

"It's always great to see you two in-person as well. Online is fun, but in-person is best." Their lockers are in a triangle on the second floor hallway. They can get an angle of the happenings from all sides, including the opposite of the hallways.

"Well, here she comes," London says.

"Who?" Jackie asks.

"Ms. 'know it all,'" London says.

"London, that's not nice," Jaylynn says.

"Maybe not nice but so true," London replies.

There is a girl named Pearse who is also in our group. She clearly gets on our nerves no matter if we are in person or online. Yuck! Why? She is always wanting to be heard.

"Good morning, everybody."

Surprisingly, no one responds.

"Good morning, Pearse," I say, to be polite.

London whispers to Jackie, "And the award goes to Jaylynn for being the nicest girl in school."

"Hush, London. She's just being nice."

"Nice, being nice to 'miss annoying'?"

"London," I whisper.

"I know," London replies.

Pearse can be very aggravating, even to our group teacher, Ms. Wright. With learning online, she often comes off mute and interrupts Ms. Wright during instructions to interject or just give a comment which is totally off of the subject or unrelated to school. London, Jackie and I roll our eyes and then communicate via private chat, talking about how Pearse gets on our nerves.

Eventually, the teacher had to place a halt to the interruptions so that she could get through the lesson. "Thank you, Pearse, for all of your comments, but as the teacher, I am required to get through the lesson, all right?"

"Yes, ma'am," Pearse replied in the chat.

"Thank you, Pearse."

While in-person for school, Ms. Wright usually only has to give that teacher look and that usually stops Pearse from interrupting.

"Ready?" Jackie asked as we close our lockers and head down the hall to class.

"Let's get to it," I reply. The three amigos, as Ms. Wright calls us, head down the hall.

As soon as we walk in the door, Ms. Wright greets us, "There are the three amigos. Back together again, safe and sound. Good morning, ladies."

"Good morning, Ms. Wright," we all three say in unison.

Ms. Wright continues to prepare for class and others come into the room slowly but surely. It's early, so kids move slow in the morning, probably from being up too late on social media.

The bell finally rings.

Ms. Wright walks over to the door and closes it. A practice that is done for multiple reasons. One, to catch the latecomers who try to sneak in, and secondly, for security reasons. After the door is closed, it is locked on the outside. Each room has a camera system that is activated only when the door is closed. The teacher must look at the panel on the screen prior to reopening the door to let anyone else in the room. We all feel safer with this new security measure, but it makes every student arrive on time because we can't slip in.

"Good morning again, everyone. Super excited to see you in person today. I trust that you had a great weekend. I did but reviewed your assignments, and overall, they were wonderful. I'll return them to you on Friday. For now, I have a new assignment, opportunity and project for you to think about and hopefully get excited about as well. I am sponsoring, along with the Museum of Art, Science and Music located right down the street, a Creatives Festival. I know that sports are a big deal in school and we all love sports, but I want to shine a spotlight on the creatives in the building and beyond. You will have the opportunity to work in groups to create a presentation that involves art, music, dance, theatre, writing and any other creative expression. I have put the requirements in a document in the Google Classroom assignments. You can form your own group. I will give you until Friday to form your own group of three to four members. If you do not have a group by Friday, I will help you form one. I hope that students on this level will be able to work together and collaborate on projects. This is a life lesson. Working with others will be a part of your job, business, organization or bake sale forever. Please review the assignment this evening, and when we meet tomorrow, I'll answer any questions that may arise," Ms. Wright explained.

'May I ask a question?' Pearse placed in the chat.

"No, Pearse, you may not ask a question today because you haven't read the requirements yet and I said that questions can be asked tomorrow. Write your questions down and then ask them tomorrow. With that being said, I will also have office hours on Friday from 11-12 and I will see you all tomorrow. Let's review our previous assignment," Ms. Wright said.

For the next thirty minutes or so, Ms. Wright handed back to each student their previous writing assignment. Even though she received each assignment electronically, Ms. Wright believed in printing them out and marking them by hand. She believed that 'old school' is still the best way for writing. She then reviewed and highlighted the good and the bad, to everyone's dismay. It was a grueling review but necessary.

"Critique, review and analysis is all of a part of getting better and, hopefully, will help you find it easier to increase, grow and format your vocabulary in your next writing pieces and be more proficient next time. Any questions?"

All of the students, including me, looked puzzled and dazed.

"I can see that you all need more practice and there is much work to be done. We still have fifteen minutes before the end of class, so review the suggestions that I have on your papers, then open your Chromebooks and begin making changes. No time will be wasted. Let's go!" Ms. Wright exclaimed.

The class realized that there would be no chit-chat today. The contest would have to wait for another day.

What does the word creative mean to you?

_____

_____

_____

_____

_____

_____

_____

_____

_____

_____

_____

_____

_____

_____

_____

_____

_____

_____

_____

Do you consider yourself creative or do you enjoy math, science instead?

_____

_____

_____

_____

_____

_____

_____

_____

_____

_____

_____

_____

_____

_____

_____

_____

_____

_____

The Assignment

When I walk in the house, my mother is busy in the living room doing what she loves.

"Hey, Jay, how was school today?"

"Okay, I guess,"

"What happened?"

"Nothing really, just a new assignment. In Ms. Wright's class, she is having us do a creative assignment which is also a festival," I explain.

"That sounds interesting."

"Yes, it does, but you know there are always things that happen with assignments."

"Like what, besides a grade?"

"Competition," I say.

"True, but a little competition is good, but bad competition can cause hurt feelings or misunderstanding."

"Or cheating," I point out.

"Do you think somebody would cheat, Jaylynn?"

"Yes, I do, but I want to do well on the project no matter what. I am picking my partners for the project carefully."

"Are your friends on board?"

"Always."

"It is great that you girls work together so well."

"We have made a pact to not compete, help each other and, no matter what, not to get mad over a boy."

"That's a good pact to have. Better than some others I've heard, but feelings are real and you must be prepared to understand them even when it comes from a close friend. Some people are better at doing some things than others. Your father and I love sports, but we're not really that athletic past walking down the street or around the park. Other people are great at sports, but we are on the sidelines cheering them on, rather than being mad or jealous. On the other hand, your father and I are creative, musical and great with technology. People pay us and others ask for our help all of the time. It is a great balance. It's great that we all don't do the exact thing at the same level but can enjoy, cheer and celebrate the accomplishments of others no matter what."

"True. Thanks, Mom, I'll keep that in mind."

"Great. Take some time to do your homework and I'm going to start dinner in about fifteen minutes,"

"Good. I'm starving. Where's Dad?"

"Should be in the kitchen. There are apples on the counter. Get one to hold you over until dinner is ready."

"Thanks, Mom.

I head down the hallway to the kitchen and, just as Mom had said, caught Dad in the kitchen eating an apple while refilling his coffee mug.

"Hey, Dad."

"Hey, sweetie, how was school?"

"Okay, and we have a school project coming up. We'll be in groups, which always starts a competition," I tell him.

"Competition, huh? Well, that takes it up another level. What's the prize?"

"Not sure yet, but I am just a little nervous about how people act when we have group projects. We'll probably get more details tomorrow."

"Okay, let me know. I am headed back to the office. You got homework?"

"Yep, I'm headed to my room to start it. Hungry, though, and the apples look great."

"They are. Try not to ruin your appetite for dinner," Dad said.

"Okay. I'll just eat one because I'm starved."

"Let's get a little work done, and then we'll eat dinner."

"Sounds like a plan."

The beauty of being in a creative family is that even though they work on their projects separately, each person supports the other, just as it should be. Mother made dinner, Dad and I cleaned up the kitchen while I brainstormed ideas for the project. They both chimed in with suggestions and cautions which had my brain spinning even more but in a good way.

After dinner, we all said goodnight and headed to our bedrooms to get ready for bed. My iPad rang, and from the icon, I could see that it was a group call with London and Jackie.

"Hey, what's up?" London asks.

"Nothing much, about to go to bed," I reply.

"Have you looked over the requirements for the Festival/Contest yet for Ms. Wright's class?" Jackie asks.

"Nope, not yet, but I talked to my parents about it. Something up?" I ask.

"Yes, the assignment is an assignment all right, but also—" Jackie starts.

"I'll finish, Jackie. It's also a competition," London interrupts and finishes for her.

"I knew it! I had a gut feeling it was going to be a competition. I hate group work anyway, no offense to you two, but it always makes us unofficially compete against each other. I hate it!" I exclaim.

"My mom says that you'll be competing with someone for something your whole life, so this is a real life assignment," London replies.

"I guess so, but it puts a lot of pressure on me and all of us," I remind her.

"Remember our pact, that we are going to work hard and stick together, no matter what. Agreed?" Jackie prompts.

"Agreed," we all say in unison.

"Jay, lights out already!" Mom calls from down the hall when she sees my light still on.

"Okay, Mom! That's it for me."

"You got to go?" London asks.

"Yes, but don't tell, because I'm going to turn out my light and read over the requirements with my handy cell phone light. It works perfectly. See you two in the morning."

"Will do," London says.

"Peace out," Jackie replies.

Are you good at starting projects early, or do you wait until the last minute?

_____

_____

_____

_____

_____

_____

_____

_____

_____

_____

_____

_____

_____

_____

_____

_____

_____

_____

If you were given a chance to work on a project like this, what would you do? Would it be something that would include Music? Artwork? Graphics? Poem? Dance of any kind? Video Presentation? Audio speech or sound? Finally, maybe a combination of multiple outlets?

_____

_____

_____

_____

_____

_____

_____

_____

_____

_____

_____

_____

_____

The Guest

Everyone arrives at school on time and super excited about the latest project. There is a buzz in the hallways and at the lockers even before class. The assignment has limited instructions so I know that there will be questions.

"Hey there, how are you all doing?" I say as I close my locker. London and Jackie's lockers are on the side of the hall.

"Fine, I guess," London replies, moaning.

"What's wrong?" I ask her.

"You know she is NOT a morning person," Jackie answers for her.

"I know, but, London, this is going to be an exciting day because of the project in Ms. Wright's class," I exclaim.

"If you say so," London replies.

"I've got my two besties with me and it's going to be a great day," I answer with a smile as I walk down the hall with London on my left and Jackie on my right.

When we walk into class, Ms. Wright is awaiting us, but there is also someone the others don't know but I know immediately.

"Good morning, everyone. Take your seats quickly. We have a special guest today whom I need to introduce to you. I know that you have questions, and we have answers."

Everyone goes to their seats, stows their belongings and become unusually quiet, anticipating what is coming next.

"Thank you so much for your attention. Our special guest is Ms. Martha Rodriguez who is the Director of Community Affairs at the Museum of Art, Science and Music. I walked around class the other day and heard your comments about not being a creative and not really being excited about participating in this project. So, I wanted her to come in, formally introduce herself and tell us a little about her creative journey. Ms. Rodriguez, the floor is yours," Ms. Wright says and signals the class to put their hands together by clapping her own two hands.

"Good morning, everyone. As Ms. Wright stated, I am Martha Rodriguez. I have been at the museum for fifteen years. My job is to coordinate, partner or, in this case, lead a project with a local organization to spotlight Music, Art and Science in this community. Ms. Wright tells me that some of you are a little reluctant, but let me explain to you all my journey in the arts. I have two creative parents. My dad was a jazz musician and my mother was a clothing designer and tailor in the area. She never went to New York but was a private collection or custom designer for people in the city so that she could still have children and maintain a home while my dad played and enjoyed life. Now, I've grown up with music, art, colored pencils, design and drawing all of my life. So it was in me. Some of you may have a creative background, some of you may have to work a little harder than others. But I want you to know that each and every one of you has an ability to come up with ideas, think and then create. You may need prompting, brainstorming from your classmates or even ideas from social media, but you can do it. I really want you to do it because discovery, brainstorming and new ideas are going to be essential for the world and your generation to lead those ideas, discoveries, inventions, new technology and the quality of life that this world will either enjoy and benefit or lag behind and suffer. So, it's bigger than an assignment or a passing grade. These are real life lessons and will have a great impact on the world around you. Any questions?"

"I have a question," Pearse says.

"Of course, she does," London whispers under her breath.

"Quiet," Ms. Wright admonishes.

"Yes, young lady, your question is?" Ms. Rodriguez replies.

"Ms. Rodriguez, what would be a winning presentation?"

"First, what's your name, young lady?"

"Pearse,"

"All right, Pearse, why do you want to win?"

"Everybody loves a winner," the girl answered.

"I get your point, and everyone does love a winner, but if you just want to create to win, that is self-centered and not global-centered. Secondly, you didn't listen to what I just said about impacting the next generation. Next, if you present the best presentation according to the specifications that Ms. Wright and I have come up with, congratulations. Finally, the main thing that you are missing out on for this project is the creative process, working with other creatives and creating something unique for others to enjoy. Do you understand?"

"Yes."

"My dad created music that people still enjoy to this day due to his recordings. My mom created designs that she used in the past and can redesign them or create something brand new, based on those designs, for new designers. My parents received payment for their work, my brothers, sisters and I were able to live a good life because of the livelihood they created, but more importantly, those creative abilities, work ethic and global outlook, I pass on to you. You then pass on what we learn in the project to others. Then it continues to someone else and others, causing the world benefit and not just stopping with you and your family. Understand?"

The students nod their heads and some even say out loud, "Yes."

"What's next, Ms. Wright?"

"Any other questions before Ms. Rodriguez goes, because we don't want to keep her."

There are no other questions.

"Well, if no other questions, let us thank Ms. Rodriguez and we will see her again in two weeks, to announce the winner, and there may be a surprise or two."

"Two surprises that I'm working on right now. Do your best and no matter what happens, you all win because you are a creative. My father used to say that creatives will eat forever because of their creations and work ethic. Let's go!"

Ms. Rodriguez gathers her purse and keys as she heads to the door.

"Robert, escort Ms. Rodriguez to the front office and out the front door," Ms. Wright says.

"Yes, ma'am," Robert replies as he gets out of his chair.

"Thank you again," Ms. Wright says.

"My pleasure," Ms. Rodriguez replies as she leaves the room.

"Now, class, it's time to get in your groups, formally brainstorm your project and get some things down on paper. Each group should have a brainstorming sheet to guide you. We have about thirty minutes left in this block. Let's begin. Anyone who isn't in a group, knows your group or needs a group, let me know."

"I need a group," Pearse says.

"I figured you did and have assigned you to be in the group with Pamela, Sharon and Sydney," the teacher says.

"I can't work alone?" Pearse asks.

"No, ma'am. There is no working alone here. This is a team effort. Pearse, you've got to learn to work with others. I know that you like doing things your way, alone and all, but that's not real life. A part of the educational system is not only teaching you the basics but how it is going to be outside of school in the real world," Ms. Wright admonishes.

"Okay, but I don't like it."

"I heard you, but if you don't do it my way, you will fail the project and won't be in the competition. Understood?"

"Yes, understood," Pearse replies. She joins the group reluctantly but her participation is very limited.

Jackie finds and tapes a larger sheet of paper on the wall and I, the artist, draws a large example of the smaller individual brainstorming sheet. We work in the corner of the room so that we can see the others' ideas but brainstorm in private.

"That's it, Jackie, I love to see your creativity at work. Make this project work best for you and your group. Now, I know that they are not the only ones. Make it work for your group as well. Get to work. Get those brain juices flowing. I love what I see so far," Ms. Wright encourages.

Ms. Wright is standing in the back of the class observing each student's actions in their group. She always loves her class being animated and noisy but, certainly, as productive as possible. This teaching style isn't for everyone, but as far as she is concerned, this is the way she learned the best and she created.

In school, when a guest speaker comes to your class or school, how do you react? Do you pay close attention or roll your eyes, expecting to be bored?

_____

_____

_____

_____

_____

_____

_____

_____

_____

_____

_____

_____

_____

_____

_____

_____

Do you like to work in groups or best alone?

_____

_____

_____

_____

_____

_____

_____

_____

_____

_____

_____

_____

_____

_____

_____

_____

_____

_____

An Advantage

The rest of that school week and the next week, London, Jackie and I worked hard each day and met virtually each night. We decided that I would provide the theme music for the project, which will play throughout our presentation. London will dance, Jackie will sing, and together, we will write something that represents our project.

There is only one more week to perfect and get everything ready for the public presentation. Because of the special project, Ms. Wright has office hours this particular Friday before school, during lunch and a short time after school. My team and I meet with Ms. Wright before school. We tell her what our presentation will look like and sound like.

"Sounds like you girls have it all figured out. I really like that you have used multiple creative outlets for your project and are not just going to present in one area. Do you have any questions for me?" Ms. Wright asks.

"I'm good. How about you, London and Jackie?" I ask, looking their way.

"I'm good too, but just so nervous," Jackie replies.

"That's totally understandable, Jackie, and from my experience, very normal. Personally, I don't like to perform unless I'm just a little nervous. The adrenaline rush keeps me on my toes, but also know that preparation helps with your nerves too. If you have worked hard, prepared yourself and trust your group members, just enjoy the moment of the presentation. Anything else?"

"No, I just want it to be over," London says.

"That's understandable too, but we only have one more week and the winner will be announced and the surprises announced too. Girls, head to your lockers and then off to class. I'll see you all later," Ms. Wright says, ending the meeting.

"Yes, ma'am," I say.

"Would one of you please shut the door on your way out?"

"London, you didn't shut it when we came in?" Jackie asks.

"I guess I must have forgotten," London answers.

"I got it," Jackie says.

"Thank you," Ms. Wright replies.

The rest of the school day went great and I got home just a little bit early. When I walk in the house, my dad has his portfolio on his back, about to head out the door.

"Hey, Jaylynn, how was school?"

"Fine and uneventful," I tell him.

"Great. What are you about to do?"

"Nothing. It's Friday and I did my homework in last period. What's up?"

"Walk with me to the museum. I have to talk to Ms. Rodriguez about a project we're working on, and maybe an exhibit or two will inspire you. Your mother is practicing and I don't want to disturb her, but we'll bring back some dinner and surprise her," he suggests.

"Sounds great, Dad."

We walk out of the building and head to the Museum of Art, Science and Music.

When we get there, Dad walks toward the office to meet Ms. Rodriguez. I stop as soon as she walks in, because a painting catches my eye immediately.

"I'll be out as soon as we finish," Dad says.

"Okay, Dad, I'll be right here," I reply. I know better than to disturb my dad, because art is his business and not just for enjoyment.

Only after a few minutes of walking through past the paintings on the wall and then heading to the next room of large displays hanging from the ceiling, I see Pearse coming through the front door. I quickly hide behind a large painting, clearly out of sight of

Pearse, and watch, as Pearse walks right up to Ms. Rodriguez's door and knocks on it. Somehow, Ms. Rodriguez's assistant is away from her desk.

"Dorothy, are you there?" Ms. Rodriguez asks from inside her office.

"No, it's Pearse," Pearse says as she opens the door.

"Excuse me, young lady, but who are you?" Ms. Rodriguez asks, quite upset.

"I was in Ms. Wright's class the other day when you came to our school and spoke," Pearse explains.

"Yes, how can I help you?"

"I want to win."

"Win what, young lady?"

"The contest and competition," Pearse says.

"The contest and competition are an added bonus, but it is still a classroom assignment and I am not your teacher."

"I know that, but I was wanting to know what you're looking for so I can do it, you select me and then I win."

As I crept closer, I could see that Dad said nothing but was completely astonished at the young lady's aggression and boldness.

"The assignment was issued to you and your classmates via Ms. Wright. I suggest that you leave this office, email your teacher and ask her these questions. Please leave this office, or I will have you escorted out," Ms. Rodriguez says.

"I was just trying to win."

"I understand that, but you don't know what a winner is. A winner is someone who works hard. If you work hard, you will always win. Not this contest, but you will win in life. Contests and competitions are complicated and based on many criteria. You need to first understand that none of your other students have come in here and demanded, unannounced and without an appointment, to ask to win. They are putting in the work, preparing themselves, practicing and following the criteria of the assignment, just as you should. That is all."

"Ms. Rodriguez, I was just—"

"Leaving, you were just leaving. Please close the door when you exit or I will have security called. You are disturbing an important meeting."

"Okay."

I watch as Pearse turns around in a huff and stomps her feet as she heads to the door. Once the door opens and she passes through it, she slams it.

***

"Oh my, how rude. I'm sorry, Garvin, but some people don't know how to trust their own creativity; they always want an advantage," Ms. Rodriguez says.

"True, but in the long run, that advantage doesn't always fit their creativity," Garvin replies.

"It's trying to force something to happen when creativity happens in the mind, hands and heart of a creative. It flows out and doesn't have to be forced."

"I totally understand."

"I see it by your work, and we are thrilled to have you on our team. So let's finish up here so you and I both can go to our homes for the night."

The meeting continued.

***

Pearse left without seeing me, but it was apparent that she was angry from the very sad face look on her face.

I thought to myself, *I don't know if I would ever be that bold.*

After I look at a few more paintings, Dad finds me and asks, "Jaylynn, you ready?"

"Yes, Dad," I reply.

When we get outside the museum, I tell him, "That girl who came out of Ms. Rodriguez's office is in my class at school."

"That's what she said when she barged into the office. She was rude and disrespectful to us both. She didn't have permission to be in the room and her request was to get an advantage that I want you to never be a part of. I want you to trust your gift. You will not always win but work on and improve your creative skills. Ask questions and get the information that the project requires, like I do. The project that I'm working on now is very specific and detailed for the client. I can't cheat because the project is custom. On the other hand, cheating is just not right. Know that your advantage is me and your mother to bounce ideas off of and help. We are always there for you and not to go around the instructions to cheat and get an unfair advantage. Understand?"

"I understand, Dad. I was wondering why she was even in the museum. I stood behind a painting so she couldn't see me. I want to win or lose on my own and not because I had an unfair advantage."

"It will pay off in the end. I promise. Let's grab a pizza and treat your mother."

"Yes, and a small salad to share. You know she will want something green besides green peppers," I say with a giggle.

"Exactly," Dad replies.

"The salad will be green, but the green on the pizza will at least be covered with cheese. My favorite," I say with a smile.

"Mine too," Dad replies with his own smile.

We both laugh as we walk faster toward the restaurant. I thought, *I am so lucky to have such great parents.*

When you hear the phrase, 'I want to get an advantage' what does that mean to you?

_____

_____

_____

_____

_____

_____

_____

_____

_____

_____

_____

_____

_____

_____

_____

_____

_____

Have you ever known someone who liked having an advantage over others? How did that make you feel?

_____

_____

_____

_____

_____

_____

_____

_____

_____

_____

_____

_____

_____

_____

Strengths and Weaknesses

Over the weekend, my group and I meet online each day to discuss the project and practice.

"That beat is great, Jaylynn," Jackie says.

"Thanks. I'm working with a student from West High who is being mentored by my mom."

"Oh wow, a high school guy," London teases.

"It's not like that, but he is cute," I muse.

"I thought so, but I agree with Jackie that the beat is very nice," London says and we all laugh.

"Okay, let's get back on track," I urge.

"Are you blushing, Jaylynn?"

"No, I'm just thinking out loud and smiling really big while I'm thinking."

"Yeah, right."

"So, Jackie, do you have the melody for the words?"

"Yes, but I need to know what you guys think," Jackie replies.

Jackie has a voice that is a dream and she sings the tune to the beat perfectly. Some of the words don't come out right, so we each suggest words so that not only can Jackie sing the words better, but the entire song will flow and rhyme just right.

Being creative is natural for all of us girls. We each bring something to the project that is unique but work so well together to make everything go even better.

True collaboration.

"Oh, well, I've got to go. I've got practice in an hour and have to go across town to the theatre," London tells us after a while.

"What are you practicing for this time?" Jackie asks.

"I want to be in the Nutcracker, for Christmas."

"Good luck to you, London. I know you'll be great!" I say.

"Thanks. By the way, Jackie, you should come down to the theatre to try out for the chorus sometime. They are looking for singers," London says.

"Sure, let me ask my mom and you send me the information."

"Will do. Bye. I'm out."

"Bye," Jackie and I say in unison.

The rest of the weekend went without a problem. I always have fun with my parents, doing what we love to do, eat, sleep and, of course, create stuff. But, on Sunday afternoon, we either head to the park or the movies for fun, just the three of us.

When we get back home, I open my laptop and find the log in for next week's classes. This week is class online, rather than in person. Although I prefer in-person school, I can go to class in my pajamas and that suits me just fine.

On Monday, Ms. Wright opens up the online meeting room at least thirty minutes early.

Normally, no one arrives in the room early, but today, Pamela does.

"Good morning, Pamela."

"Good morning, Ms. Wright," she responds.

"What brings you on so early?"

"I have something to tell you."

"Okay, go ahead," Ms. Wright says.

"We can't work with Pearse."

"I know that she can be difficult, but team work is a critical part of how life really works beyond school. You will need to work with others throughout your life, so why not learn how now?"

"Ms. Wright, I'm all about that, but not this."

"What do you mean?"

Pamela explains everything that has been going on with and during their group meetings with Pearse in attendance, and it isn't good.

"Ms. Wright, we don't sing, play an instrument or any of that. We are writers, that's it. We can put what we write to music, but our strength is writing, period."

"I understand, and that's what this is all about, being creative and presenting your strengths as a creative and not focusing on the competition. I think that my mistake was even telling you all that it was a competition, rather than focusing on being creative. I'll admit that and will let the class know it too."

"Can we either start over or work by ourselves?"

"I give you permission this time to work with your initial group and go back to your original plan. Say nothing to Pearse because I'll meet with her. Thank you for letting me know. I appreciate you being brave enough to tell me what was going on. I'll take care of it."

"Thank you, Ms. Wright. I appreciate you being honest with me too. I don't know many teachers who would say that."

"You're welcome, and thank you, Pamela, for saying that. Go ahead and stay in the room, but put yourself on mute."

Ms. Wright's cell phone buzzed, indicating a text, 'call me when you're free.'

She responded, 'will do. I'm in class right now but will have a break in 2 hours.'

The response was, 'great.'

The beauty of the virtual space is that you can have multiple conversations at the same time anonymously. Ms. Wright needed to be able to communicate with her students, prepare for class and connect with parents, administrators or other personnel if necessary. There were other students who were logging in, but they weren't permitted to join until let into the room by the teacher only.

All of the students began to gather in the room. Somehow the 'chat' was open.

"Hello, everyone, and I look forward to winning and taking home the trophy for the

Arts Project. We are going to have a great day."

The comment was seen by Ms. Wright, copied and immediately deleted. All students had the ability to see the chat comment but only a few could see it.

"Good morning, everyone. Pearse, comments like that will not be permitted in the chat and we will have a discussion after this session. Let's talk about our latest assignment, but before that, these groups still need to report to me the status of their project. Office hours will be posted and I will email each of you. I also want to say that I believe I have made an error by even telling you all that there was a competition that was a part of this assignment.

I thought it would inspire you, but instead, it has overshadowed the real purpose, and that is for you to present your best, play to your strength and not your weakness, and be as creative as possible, but the competition has somehow tarnished that. I'll have to discuss with Ms. Rodriguez what to do about that, but for now, I want you to work hard, but don't focus on a prize, winning or beating anyone but yourself. Now, let's begin." Ms. Wright was quite irritated. The students could tell, even virtually. Because of Pearse's comment, Ms. Wright had to address it, but Pearse's behavior shouldn't cause a problem for the others. Ultimately, it was her professional responsibility to teach and deal with Pearse later.

Two hours later, Ms. Wright spoke with Ms. Rodriguez and she had more information about the Pearse objective, motives and actual participation level in the assignment and competition.

"Well, first, let me apologize for my student and her actions."

"No need to apologize because you had no part in it, but we now see how far people will go to win a competition."

"Also, we see how people will focus on winning rather than taking their own gifts and working on them to be the best that they can be but, instead, get an unfair advantage or, let's be honest, cheat," Ms. Wright said.

"Right."

"I'll handle my end with this student. Thank you for calling me."

"No problem. I respect her boldness because if put to good use and in the right situation, it can really work for her. In this case, not so much."

"Not at all. Have a great rest of the day."

"You too."

Ms. Wright now has the unpopular task that all teachers must face, and that is to discuss with the principal the next steps regarding the behavior of a student. Then, next, meeting with Pearse and her parents.

What do you think will happen with Pearse? Should she participate in the contest? What should her grade be?

_____

_____

_____

_____

_____

_____

_____

_____

_____

_____

_____

_____

_____

_____

_____

_____

How far are you willing to go to win?

_____
_____
_____
_____
_____
_____
_____
_____
_____
_____
_____
_____
_____
_____
_____
_____
_____
_____
_____

Practice Makes Perfect

The rest of the week was filled with excitement, meetings, rehearsals and nerves. One person's life wasn't so exciting, and that was Pearse's. Her parents were called into the school.

"Mr. and Mrs. Norton, please have a seat," said Mrs. Simpson, who was the principal. The counselor, Ms. Turner, and Ms. Wright were also in attendance, along with Pearse and her parents.

"Thank you so much. I don't why we're here," Mr. Norton, Pearse's dad, stated. Mrs. Norton, Pearse's mom, appeared confused as well.

"Well, you do understand the assignment that Pearse has in Ms. Wright's class," the principal began.

"No, I don't know about the assignment," Mr. Norton said.

"Ms. Wright, will you explain?"

"Good morning, Mr. and Mrs. Norton. Have you ever signed into the Parent Portal that has your child's classes listed, assignments, grades, calendar and upcoming events posted there?"

"No, we have not. We have very competitive jobs that are important to our careers and household. We trust our daughter Pearse completely," Mrs. Norton said.

"I am thrilled to hear that you trust your daughter, but children need guidance in the maturing process," Ms. Turner, the counselor, interjected.

"We have taught her from a child and sacrificed a lot for her, but feel we need to provide for the household, so Pearse is old enough now to be able to do things on her own, and that includes her education," Mr. Norton said.

Ms. Wright now knew why Pearse acted and did the things that she did in school and outside of school. In spite of their parenting skills, Ms. Wright went thoroughly through the assignment, the museum, as well as Pearse's behavior by going to the museum and interrupting Ms. Rodriguez's meeting in her office.

Ms. Turner provided the log in information for the portal. Mrs. Simpson issued the discipline.

"Mr. and Mrs. Norton, we are not here to tell you how to raise your child but do encourage you to be as proactive and involved as you can possibly be. Pearse's actions are not only a reflection of you, but of this school, and jeopardize our community relationships with the museum. With that being said, Pearse will not be able to participate in the competition portion of the assignment but should complete the assignment for the course. She will present to her class but not to the museum community."

"Daddy, do something!" Pearse yelled.

"Calm down, Pearse. I believe that is a bit harsh, don't you think?" Mr. Norton said.

"No, I do not, especially when she jeopardized her safety by being in the museum, underage, unaccompanied, interrupted a business meeting and aggressively demanded to know how she could win the competition and not for tips on how to do well on a school assignment,"

"Winning is everything in our house, and we encourage Pearse to do her best to win," Mrs. Norton said.

"In this case, Pearse was not doing her best to win, but doing her best to get an advantage, which is not a part of the assignment or our educational standards. Good day, Mr. and Mrs. Norton," Mrs. Simpson said as she walked out of the conference room.

Ms. Wright and Ms. Turner followed the principal's lead and left the room, with Pearse and her parents sitting there trying to figure out what just happened.

***

Meanwhile, in my life, the next day, after a long week of practice online and in-person, my parents have a surprise for me. My mom called London and Jackie's parents and invited them to the house on Saturday afternoon. At 3:00 p.m., the doorbell rang and Dad buzzed them in and opened the front door. Shortly thereafter, the elevator bell dinged and exiting the elevator, was London and her parents, along with Jackie and her parents.

"Come on in. Glad to have you all," Garvin Harris said with a smile while holding open the door.

"Welcome, welcome," Montana Harris greeted each one.

I came into the room and asked, "What's going on?"

"Well, we have a surprise for you all."

"You have worked so hard these past few weeks. I wanted to give you girls an opportunity to perform your presentation in front of us. No critique, just support. Then pizza, salad and brownies. Does that sound good?" Ms. Montana asked.

"Yes, but we are not really prepared to perform tonight."

"Jackie has been practicing all week."

"London has been dancing up a storm."

"Well, it sounds like you guys are more than ready."

"Jaylynn, take them into your room, get everything ready, and you've got about twenty minutes. Go," Dad tells us.

"What about our costumes?"

"Don't worry about costumes, just do your best."

"I can't wait to see it all together. I feel like I've been seeing one third of something great but wanted to put the other pieces together also," Jackie's mom says.

The ladies go into the kitchen to help Mom any way that they can. The dads stay in the living room talking about sports and work.

Exactly twenty minutes later, we appear with our music, drawing and writing, to begin.

"We're ready!" I announce.

Everyone sits down to watch the performance. Fortunately, our home has the sound acoustics for performances and music as well as space enough to dance. Not a full stage, but space enough.

When we finish, our parents give us a round of applause, congratulations all around and encouragement to just do what we performed tonight on the day of the presentation.

"That was wonderful, girls. No matter what happens in the competition, you have done your best and I'm so proud of you all," my dad told us.

"Thanks, Dad."

"Thanks, Mr. Harris," my friends echo.

"Are we ready for pizza?"

"Yes!" everyone exclaims.

"I'd like to make a toast. If you all could raise your very plastic cups," Dad says as we all laugh.

He continues, "To our daughters, the creatives. As a fellow creative, you have made my heart glad. I am thrilled to know that the future of these creatives is extremely bright. Thank you for using your gift for positivity and the world of art."

"Cheers! Hear, hear. Congratulations and good job," are just some of the responses to Dad's toast.

We all continue to eat until we are full and then enjoy movies until everyone is drowsy and ready to go home to bed.

"Goodnight all," my family says as we watch the Owens's and the Greens head toward the elevator.

"Thanks, Mom and Dad," I say when they are gone.

"You're welcome, love."

"Now, I have one request. We are all sleepy and tired, but we only have a little to do to clean up the kitchen. You guys in?" Mom asks.

"Yep, let's get it done," Dad replies.

The three of us have little to do to clean up because the other parents helped so much, but we always love being together, no matter what we are doing.

Creatives create. What are you creating? If nothing now, what do you want to create?

_____

_____

_____

_____

_____

_____

_____

_____

_____

_____

_____

_____

_____

_____

_____

_____

_____

Finally, It's Presentation Day!

The day finally arrived that we have all been waiting for, and that is to perform our creative representation in front of Ms. Rodriguez, our parents, teachers and the entire school. Everybody is nervous, and the entire school is buzzing with excitement about the presentations. First, we are able to be in school together and not watch online. Secondly, and most importantly for all school assemblies, is that we aren't in class.

Ms. Wright's classroom is the central hub and place for the presenters to get ready.

"I'm so nervous, I can hardly stand it," I say.

"Me too," London adds.

"I'm always nervous, but nerves are the adrenalin I need to do what I need to do," Jackie says.

"Jackie, you sing on stages all of the time, and London acts, but I'm not used to it like you are."

"I know, but here's how I do it. I pick a spot above the crowd and keep my eye on it."

"How does that work when I'm dancing on the stage from one end to the other?" London asks.

"Yeah, and I'm reading my piece!" I exclaim.

"Well, I guess that wouldn't work for you guys. Let me go with this. Know that I love you both and we're going to be great."

"Jackie, what are we going to do with you?"

"Love me back. Let's go!"

It seems all of the groups look and feel the same way. Nerves are all over the place and everyone is just wanting to get it over with.

The librarian is handling music and any media needed for the presentations. The principal is to greet the guests and lead them to the auditorium. The maintenance department has the building spotless for the event.

Ms. Wright looks at the clock and knows that it's time to get backstage.

"Attention, everyone. It's time to head to the auditorium and backstage. No talking once we leave the room, and you'll be able to greet your friends and family once everything is over. Understand?"

"Understand," all of the classmates respond and agree.

"Now, get in a circle really quickly. Look at the person to your left and right. Now, repeat after me. You've practiced. You're prepared. Now do your best and present! Say it!"

It sounds weird to repeat what Ms. Wright said, but surprisingly, it settles us down, so we say it three times, "You've practiced. You're prepared. Now do your best and present!"

"All right, let's go. Get everything that you need. Get in a straight line. Quiet, everyone. Jacob, hold the door for everyone. Silence!

Let's go!" Ms. Wright says as she exits the door and leads the way.

Everyone is in their places backstage and the auditorium is filled.

"Welcome, everyone, to the first of many presentations by our phenomenal creatives here at Felpps Academy. Special thanks to Ms. Wright and her classes, along with our special guests, Ms. Rodriguez from the Museum of Art, Science and Music, and she has brought along two other board members. No pressure to anyone, but do your best. Students, be attentive and gracious to the presenters, along with our guests. Ms. Wright, would you please come forward, give greetings and make the introductions," Ms. Simpson, the principal begins.

"Thank you, Principal Simpson. I am honored to present the students from my Creative Arts Classes. They have worked hard and I am super excited to present their creative expressions to you all. Thank you to Ms. Rodriguez and her guests for the partnership and encouragement for this project. Now, to the best part. Each student group will present their creative expression through music, writing, dance, singing and/or visual arts. Sit, back, relax and enjoy," Ms. Wright says, to a resounding applause from the audience.

Each presentation is wonderful and a standing ovation is given at the end of the presentation.

So what do you think happened at the end? What would you have liked to have seen happen at the end?

Who will win?

The Winner Is...

Everyone!

Now, I know that you wanted a clear winner because everyone loves a winner. But the real winner in this story is everyone who had the skill, courage and tenacity to create something, whether it was a song, a writing piece, music, dance steps, draw some art or a combination of all of these creative expressions. That is the point and mission of this story, for each of you who reads it, shares it and listens to it, to create something.

Use your imagination. Listen to some music and let your body express itself while listening to the music.

Get out your pen, paper, mobile device or phone and put words into the atmosphere to express what you're feeling, inspire someone to be greater or to make us laugh or cry with your words so much that they take us to a faraway land.

Tune up your instrument. Put the chords in harmony or dissonance and make the music that is in your soul spill out in the world for all to enjoy.

The goal of a creative with creativity is to create. Let's go!

Epilogue

I really want you to think about what the ending should, or could be, but I can't leave the end of the story up in the air like that.

So turn the page and find out how I really want the story to end.

Julia Royston

All of the student presentations ended with a standing ovation by the crowd. Ms. Wright was overwhelmed with emotion but managed to introduce Ms. Rodriguez and the other two guests to come to the stage.

"Wow, what incredible performances by our students. Thank you for the awesome creativity displayed on the stage today. I want to introduce the representatives from the Museum of Art, Science and Music . I feel like Ms. Rodriguez is a part of us now so would you be so kind as to introduce the guests you brought with you?" Ms. Wright said as she handed Ms. Rodriguez the microphone.

"Thank you to Ms. Wright. First, let me thank Ms. Wright and her students for all of their hard work. The future is bright with these phenomenal creatives. Secondly, thank you to Ms. Simpson for allowing us into her school and partnering for this endeavor. Finally, let me introduce Ms. French and Mr. Roberts. These two are members of our board and I believe Mr. Roberts has an announcement."

"Thank you, Ms. Rodriguez. It was a pleasure experiencing these wonderful young people's presentations this morning. Congratulations to you all and especially the students and their parents. It was so wonderful to see your creative minds at work. Ms. French and I have working on a project that we would like to invite you all to participate in. As you know, the Annual Music Festival for the Holidays is coming up and we have been given the opportunity to present young artists to the city. With your parents' permission, I would like Ms. Wright's students to participate on stage."

The auditorium erupted along with the students still on stage. The opportunity was definitely unexpected and overwhelming.

Ms. French chimed in, "Please let Ms. Wright know that you would like to participate and we'll send her more information. You have another month to prepare for this performance. Congratulations are in order."

Jaylynn and her group, along with the rest of the class, could hardly focus the rest of the school day because of their excitement.

When Jaylynn finally got home from school, her parents had her favorite meal on the table and, with their glasses of fruit punch in their hands, lifted them for a toast.

"To our lovely daughter for her performance," Ms. Montana Harris said.

"To our wonderful daughter, Jaylynn, the creative. We love you more than life. I told you, love, that if you do your best, good things can happen and will happen to you. Congratulations," Mr. Harris said.

"Thank you, and I love you too. This apple hasn't fallen too far from your own creative trees," Jaylynn said as she beamed.

About the Author

 Julia Royston spends her days doing what she loves, writing, publishing, speaking and coaching others to Get Their Message to the Masses and Turn Their Words into Wealth.

Julia has written 72 books and co-authored 8, recorded 3 music CDs and coached more than 250 to write and publish books as well as establish their own businesses. She is the owner of five companies and a non-profit as well as the host of "Live Your Best Life" heard each Sunday morning at 10:00 a.m. EST and "The Book Business Boss Show" on Tuesdays at 10:30 a.m. EST. Both shows are on www.envision-radio.com and she is a contributing author to Envision Radio Magazine.

To stay connected with Julia, visit www.juliaakroyston.com.

Other Books by Julia A. Royston

Made in the USA
Columbia, SC
12 February 2023

11735790R00065